The Complete Guitar Player Eric Clapton Songbook

by Arthur Dick.

Wise Publications
London/New York/Sydney

Exclusive Distributors:
Music Sales Limited
8/9 Frith Street, London, W1V 5TZ, England
Music Sales Pty. Limited
120 Rothschild Avenue, Rosebery, NSW 2018, Australia

This book © Copyright 1991 by Wise Publications
Order No. AM83593
ISBN 0.7119.2540.2

Cover design by Pearce Marchbank Studio
Arranged by Arthur Dick
Compiled by Peter Evans
Music processed by Musicprint

Front cover photograph by Geoff Swaine

Music Sales' complete catalogue lists thousands of
titles and is free from your local music book shop, or direct from
Music Sales Limited. Please send a cheque/postal order for £1.50 for postage to
Music Sales Limited, Newmarket Road, Bury St Edmunds, Suffolk IP33 3YB.

Your Guarantee of Quality
As publishers, we strive to produce every book to the highest
commercial standards.
All the music has been freshly engraved, and the book has been
carefully designed to minimise awkward page turns, and to make
playing from it a real pleasure.
Particular care has been given to specifying acid-free, neutral-
sized paper which has not been elemental chlorine bleached but produced
with special regard for the environment. Throughout, the printing
and binding have been planned to ensure a sturdy, attractive
publication which should give years of enjoyment.
If your copy fails to meet our high standards, please inform us and
we will gladly replace it.

We've Been Told (Jesus Is Coming)

Traditional. Arranged by Eric Clapton

4/4 Rhythm Strumming
See Course Book No. 1 Page 12.

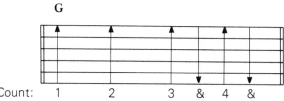

Count: 1   2   3 & 4 &

3

Let It Rain

Words & Music by Eric Clapton & Bonnie Bramlett

4/4 Rhythm Strumming
See Course Book No. 1 Page 14.

Lyrics:

The rain is fall-ing through the mist of sor-row that sur-round-ed me. The sun could melt the fog a-way, the mist that may sur-round me. Let it rain; let it rain. Let your love rain down on me. Let it rain; let it rain.. Let it rain, rain, rain. My rain, rain.

Solo Guitar

(Let ring)

D.%. al Coda

⊕ *CODA*

let it rain, ___ rain, ___ rain. ___ Let it rain;

let it rain. ___ Let your love ___ rain down on me. ___

Let it rain; ___ let it rain, ___ Let it rain ___ rain,

Repeat to Fade
with ad lib. Guitar Solo

Guitar 1

Guitar 2

rain.

Verse 2
My life was like a desert flower
Burning in the sun.
Until I found the way to love,
This heart was sad and done.
(*Chorus:* Let it rain *etc.*)

Verse 3 (on %.)
Now I know the secret
There is nothing that I lack
If I give my love to you,
Be sure to give it back.
(*Chorus:* Let it rain *etc.*)

5

Bell Bottom Blues

Words & Music by Eric Clapton

4/4 Rhythm/Simple Arpeggio
See Course Book No. 1 Page 27.

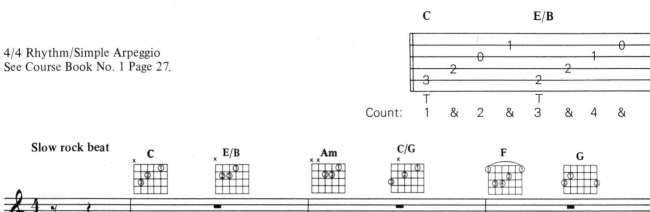

Slow rock beat

Bell Bot-tom Blues, you made me cry.__ I don't want to lose __ this feel - in'. If I could choose__ a place to die,__ it would be in __ your arms.__

Do you wan - na see me crawl a - cross__ the floor _____ to you?

Do you wan-na hear me beg you to take me back?__ I'd glad - ly do it be-cause

I don't want to fade a - way.__ Give me one __ more day, _____ please.

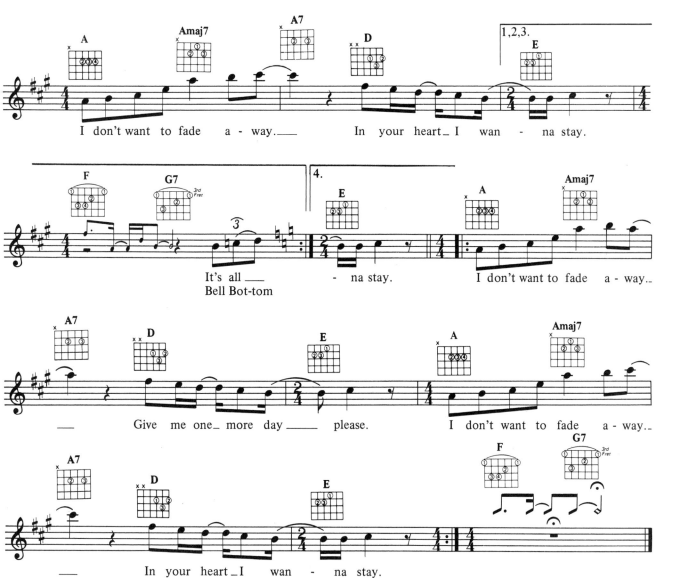

Verse 2
It's all wrong, but it's all right
The way that you treat me baby.
Once I was strong, but I lost the fight
You won't find a better loser.

Verse 3 Instrumental

Verse 4
Bell Bottom Blues, don't say goodbye
I'm sure we're gonna meet again.
And if we do, don't ya be surprised
If you find me with another lover.

I Can't Stand It Words & Music by Eric Clapton

4/4 Rhythm/Strumming (accent beats 2 and 4)
See Course Book No. 1 Page 14.

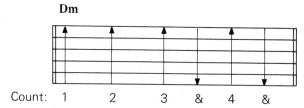

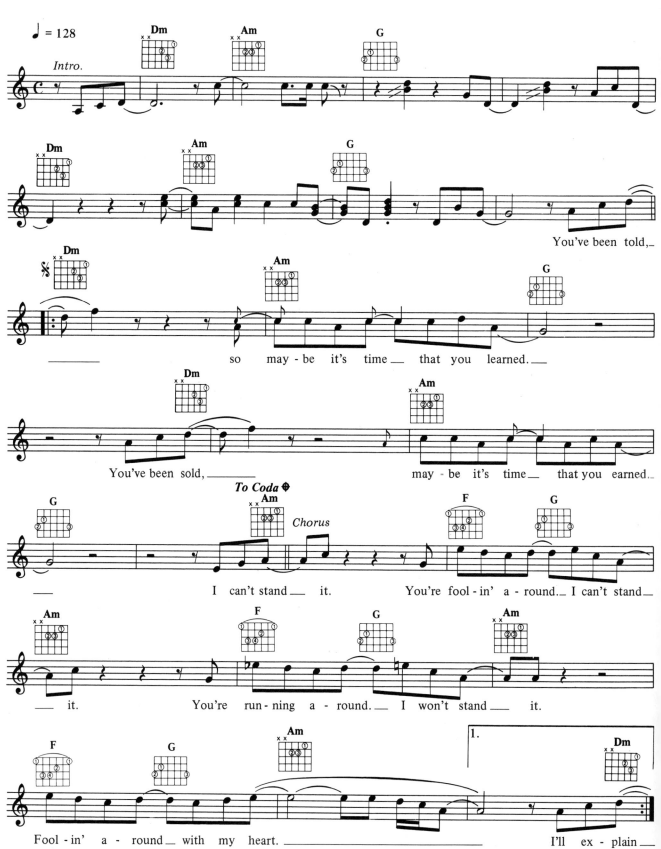

You've been told,__

so may-be it's time__ that you learned.__

You've been sold,_____ may-be it's time__ that you earned.__

I can't stand__ it. You're fool-in' a-round.__ I can't stand__

__ it. You're run-ning a-round.__ I won't stand__ it.

Fool-in' a-round__ with my heart._____ I'll ex-plain

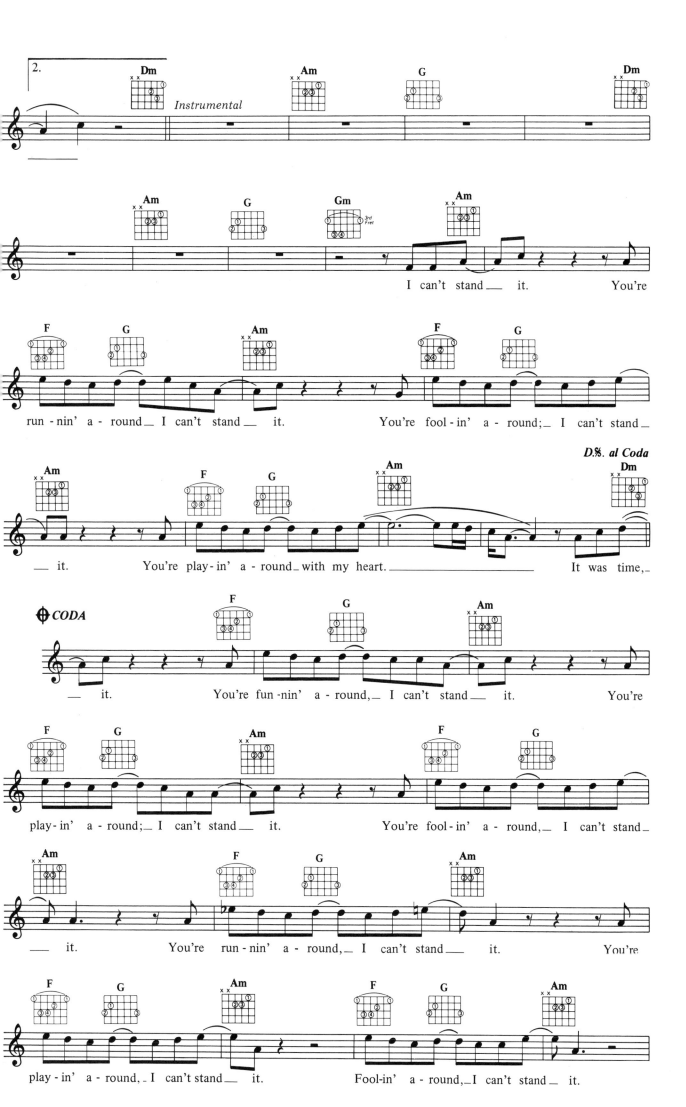

Verse 2
I'll explain, I feel like I'm bein' used
Make it plain, so you don't get confused.

Chorus 2
I can't stand it
Foolin' around I won't stand it
You're running around I can't stand it
Foolin' around with my heart.

Verse 3 (on %.)
It was time, time for me to let you know
Ain't no crime, no crime to let your feelings show.

CODA – Chorus 3 al Fine

She's Waiting
Words & Music by Eric Clapton & Peter Robinson

4/4 Rhythm pattern/Arpeggios
See Course Book No. 2 Pages 10/11 and 20

11

ing

for an-oth-er love._

song._

She's wait - ing

Repeat with Vocal ad lib.

for an-oth-er love. ____

She's wait -

Verse on S.
I see the hunger burning in her eyes.
Any fool could see there's something wrong
You keep pretending not to care,
Well, I will hear you sing a different song.

Bottle Of Red Wine
Words & Music by Eric Clapton & Bonnie Bramlett

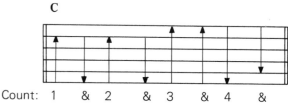

4/4 Rhythm/Strumming/Swing feel/Accent beats 2 and 4
See Course Book No. 2 Page 5.

Count: 1 & 2 & 3 & 4 &

Bright blues rock

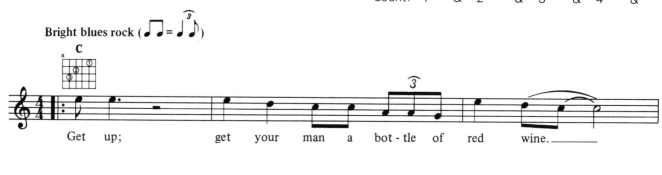

Get up; get your man a bot-tle of red wine.___

Get up; get your man a bot-tle of red wine.___

I can't get up out of bed ___ with this cra-
You hear what I say? ___ Gon-

zy feel-ing in my head. ___
na love you a-ny - way. ___

Get up;

get your man a bot-tle of red wine. ___

I went to an all - night get ___ to-ge - ther, ___

and ev-'ry - one ___ I knew___ was there. ___

Had the love that will last for-ev - er.____

Ev-'ry - where ___ I looked, ___ I saw you stand-ing there. ____

Instrumental

D.C. (Lyric 1) al Coda

CODA

Get up right now.____

Verse 2
Get up; get your man a bottle of red wine
Get up; get your man a bottle of red wine
You hear what I say?
Gonna love you anyway.
Get up; get your man a bottle of red wine.

Verse 3 — D.C. as Verse 1

The Shape You're In   Words & Music by Eric Clapton

4/4 Rhythm/Strumming/Swing
See Course Book No. 2 Page 15.

Bright blues shuffle

took my ba-by to see_ a show._   She_ was tell-in' me she did-n't

wan-na go._   I said "Come on, girl,_ what's the mat - ter with you?"_

But I could tell by the smell   that she'd had a few.

1.   A hold on,   ba-by, don't you) get too_ tight._   You start-ed ear-ly and we've
2.3. I sing, hold on,   girl,_   don't _ {

got all   night_ You got-ta   take it ea-sy,   take it slow._   We don't want the whole

world to know_ a-bout the   shape you're in._   Hey,   babe_ } the
girl,_ } ba-by,

Verse 2
My little girl really loves that wine
Wine will do it to her most every time
If it's red or white, if it's inbetween
She can drink more wine than I've ever seen.

Bridge
I sing, hold on, girl, don't get too tight *etc.*

Verse 3 on ⅘.
I'm not tryin' to get heavy with you
I'll mind my own business if you want me to.
But I love you girl, I don't love no one else
I'm just tellin' you, baby, 'cause I've been there myself.

Bridge
I sing, hold on, girl, don't get too tight *etc.*

17

Wonderful Tonight

Words & Music by Eric Clapton

4/4 Rhythm/Arpeggio
See Course Book No. 2 Page 20.

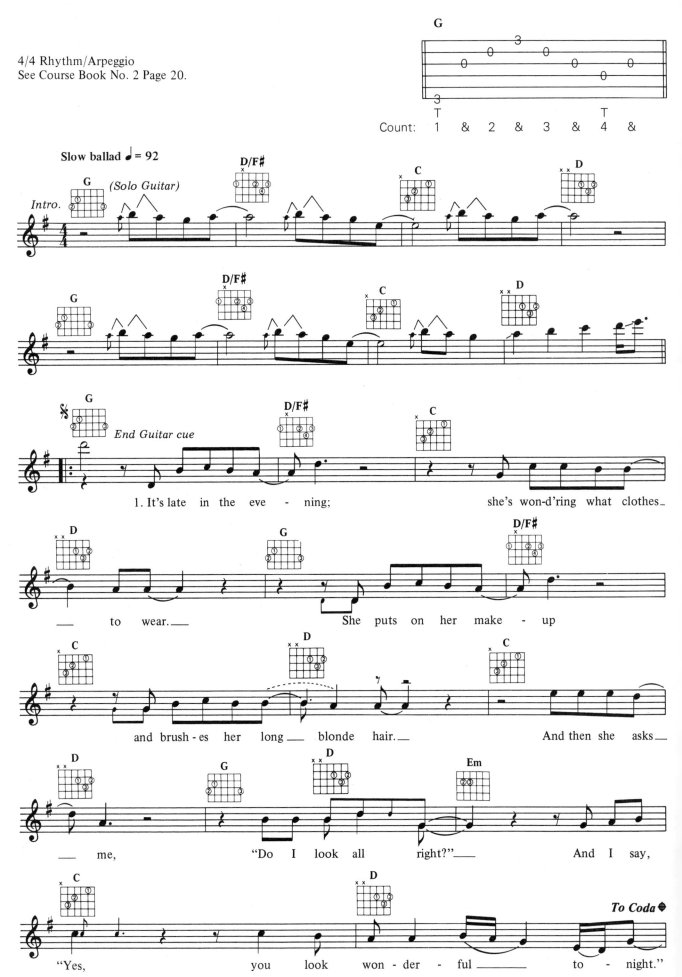

Slow ballad ♩ = 92

Intro.

(Solo Guitar)

End Guitar cue

1. It's late in the eve - ning; she's won-d'ring what clothes___ ___ to wear.___ She puts on her make - up and brush - es her long ___ blonde hair.___ And then she asks___ ___ me, "Do I look all right?"___ And I say, "Yes, you look won - der - ful _____ to - night."

To Coda ⊕

18

Verse 2
We go to a party, and everyone turns to see
This beautiful lady is walking around with me
And then she asks me "Do you feel all right?"
And I say, "Yes I feel wonderful tonight."

Verse 3 on ℅.
It's time to go home now, and I've got an aching head.
So I give her the car keys and she helps me to bed.
And then I tell her, as I turn out the light,
I say, "My darling, you are wonderful tonight."

19

Knockin' On Heaven's Door
Words & Music by Bob Dylan

4/4 Rhythm/Strumming/Swing
See Course Book No. 2 Page 8

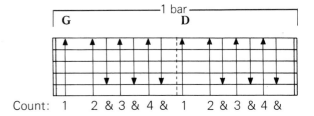

INTRODUCTION
Freely slowly

Bright tempo *(with Rhythm)*

VERSE

1. 3. Ma,   take this badge off of me

I can't use__ it a - ny - more.__   It's get-tin' dark,__ too dark ta

see.   I feel like I'm knock-in' on hea-ven's door.__ Knock knock knock-

CHORUS

To Coda

Knock, knock knockin' on hea-ven's door,__   knock, knock, knockin' on hea-ven's door.__
in'

Knock, knock, knock-in' on hea-ven's door __

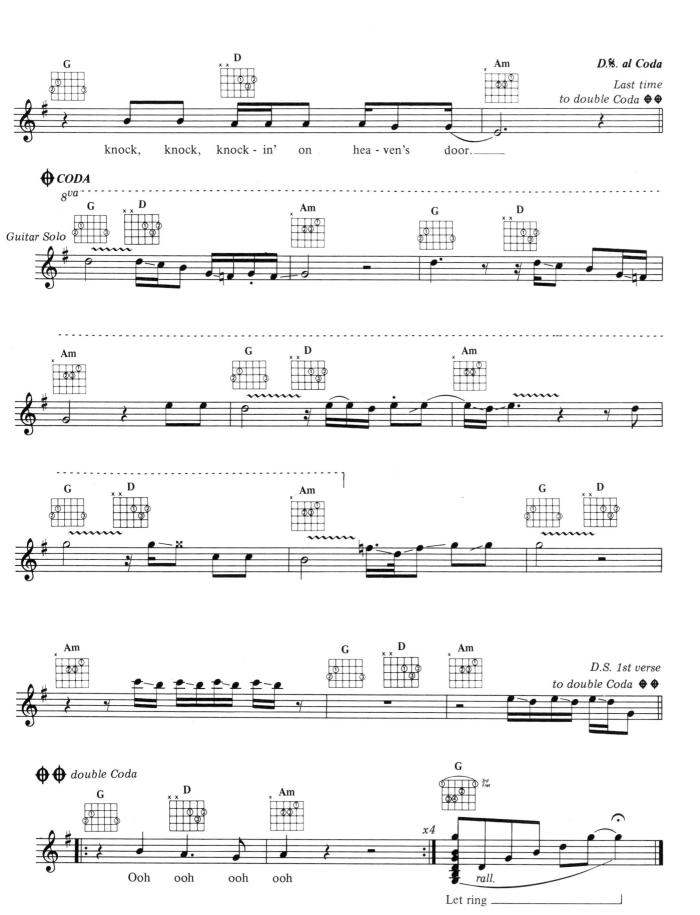

knock, knock, knock - in' on hea - ven's door.

CODA

Guitar Solo

Ooh   ooh   ooh   ooh

Verse 2
Ma, take these guns away from me
I can't shoot them anymore.
There's a long black cloud following me
I feel like I'm knockin' on heaven's door.

Verse 3 on 𝄋. as Verse 1

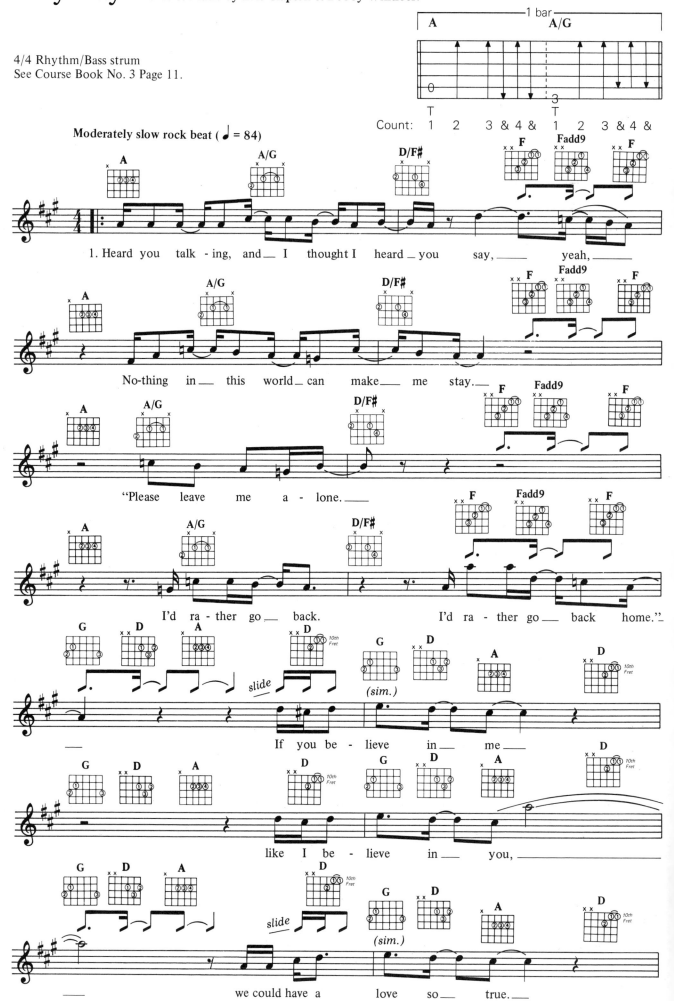

Any Day Words & Music by Eric Clapton & Bobby Whitlock

4/4 Rhythm/Bass strum
See Course Book No. 3 Page 11.

Count: 1 2 3 & 4 & 1 2 3 & 4 &

Moderately slow rock beat (♩ = 84)

1. Heard you talk - ing, and __ I thought I heard __ you say, _____ yeah, _____

No - thing in __ this world __ can make __ me stay. __

"Please leave me a - lone. __

I'd ra - ther go __ back. I'd ra - ther go __ back home."

If you be - lieve in __ me __

like I be - lieve in __ you,

we could have a love so __ true. __

Chorus (sung all times)

Full Rhythm

We would go on end-less-ly.___ And I know,___

___ a-ny day,___ a-ny day,___ I will see_you smile.___

1,2,3.

A-ny-way,_ a-ny-way,_ on-ly for a lit-tle while._

4.

Extra Choruses

A-ny day_ a-ny day,___ I will see you smile.___

Repeat 3x

A-ny way_ a-ny way_ only for a little while._

slide

Verse 2
Someday, baby, I know you're gonna need me,
When this old world has got you down.
I'll be right here; so woman, call me,
And I'll never ever let you down.
If you believe in me (*etc.*)

Verse 4
Break the glass and twist the knife into yourself.
You gotta be a fool to understand:
To bring your woman back home after she's left you for another,
You gotta be a man.
If you believe in me (*etc.*)

Verse 3 — Instrumental (vocal joins at chorus)

Badge

Words & Music by Eric Clapton & George Harrison

4/4 Rhythm/Bass-strum + Arpeggios
See Course Book No. 3 Pages 11 and 16

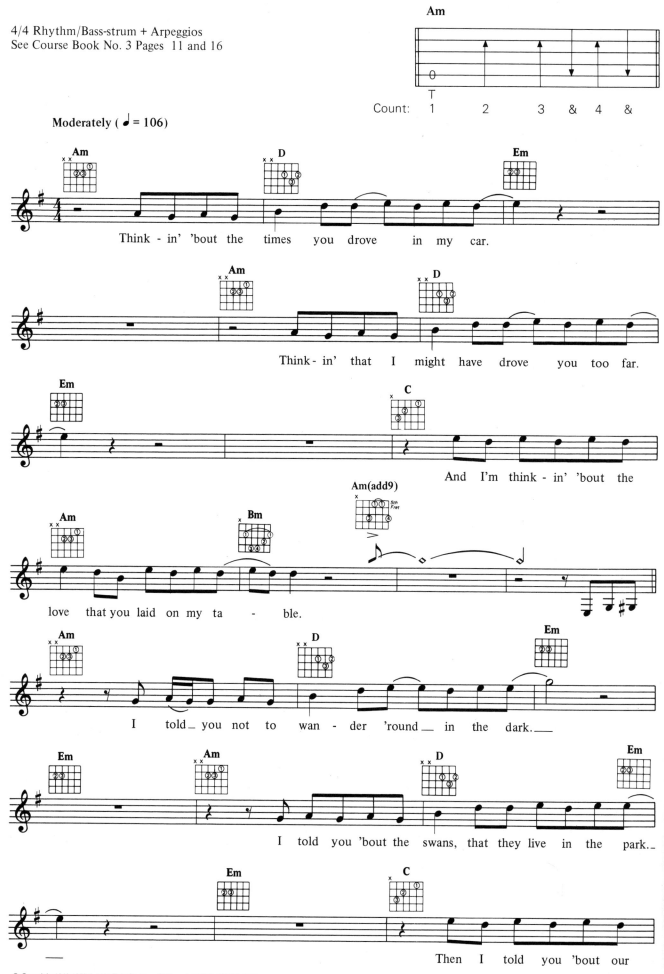

Moderately (♩ = 106)

Think - in' 'bout the times you drove in my car.

Think - in' that I might have drove you too far.

And I'm think - in' 'bout the

love that you laid on my ta - ble.

I told you not to wan - der 'round in the dark.

I told you 'bout the swans, that they live in the park.

Then I told you 'bout our

I Shot The Sheriff   Words & Music by Bob Marley

4/4 Rhythm/Syncopated/Accented off beats
See Course Book No. 3 Pages 6-8.

1,2.

N.C.

3.

N.C.

D.℘. al Coda

⊕ CODA

N.C.

Gm
3rd Fret

I shot the she - riff

Cm7
3rd Fret

Gm
3rd Fret

Gm
3rd Fret

but I did not shoot no dep - u - ty.

I shot the she - riff

Cm7
3rd Fret

Ebmaj7
3rd Fret

Dm7

Gm
3rd Fret

Repeat to Fade

but I did - n't shoot no dep - u - ty.

Guitar Solo

Verse 2
Sheriff John Brown always hated me,
For what, I don't know.
And every time that I plant a seed
He said, "Kill it before it grows."
"Kill it before it grows."

Verse 3
Freedom came our way one day
So I started out of town
All of a sudden I see Sheriff John Brown
Aimin' to shoot me down.
So I shot, I shot him down.

Verse 2 on ℘.
Reflexes got the better of me
What will be will be
Ev'ry day the bucket goes to the well
One day the bottom will drop out
I say, one day the bottom will drop out.

Lay Down Sally

Words & Music by Eric Clapton, Marcy Levy & George Terry

4/4 Rhythm/Strumming/Lively
See Course Book No. 3 Pages 10 & 11.

♩ = 188

1. There is no-thing that ___ is wrong ___ in want-ing you ___ to stay ___ here ___ with me. I know you've got ___ some-where ___ to go, ___ but won't you make ___ your-self ___ at home ___ and stay with me? ___ And don't you ev-er leave. ___ Lay down Sal-ly and rest here in ___ my arms. ___ Don't you ___ think ___ you want ___ some-one ___ to talk ___ to? Lay down Sal-ly, no need to leave ___ so soon. ___ I've been try-ing all ___ night long ___ just to

talk to you.—

The talk to you.—

Repeat 16x
D.S. al Coda

CODA

talk to you.—   Lay down Sal - ly   and rest here in— my arms.—

— Don't you think you want— some - one— to talk— to?

Lay down Sal - ly,   no need to leave— so soon.—   I've been try - ing all—

(Rhythm pattern
Repeat to Fade)

— night long — just to talk to you.—

Verse 2
The sun ain't nearly on the rise
And we still got the moon and stars above.
Underneath the velvet skies
Love is all that matters —
Won't you stay with me?
And don't you ever leave.

Verse 3 on %.
I long to see the morning light
Colouring your face so dreamily
So don't you go and say goodbye
You can lay your worries down —
And stay with me?
And don't you ever leave.

Why Does Love Got To Be So Sad?

Words & Music by Eric Clapton & Bobby Whitlock

4/4 Rhythm/Strumming/Fast
Syncopated chord changes
See Course Book No. 3 Page 7

Count: 1 2 3 & 4 & 1 2 3 & 4 &

Moderately in 2 (♩ = 116)
(or fast 4 as in the rhythm count)

Got to find me a way, ___ take me back to yes-

ter - day. ___ How can I ev - er hope ___ to for - get ___

___ you? Won't you show me a place ___

where I can hide my lone - ly ___ face. I know you're gon - na

break my heart ___ if I let ___ you.

Why does love ___ got to be so ___ sad?

Why does love ___ got to be so ___ sad?

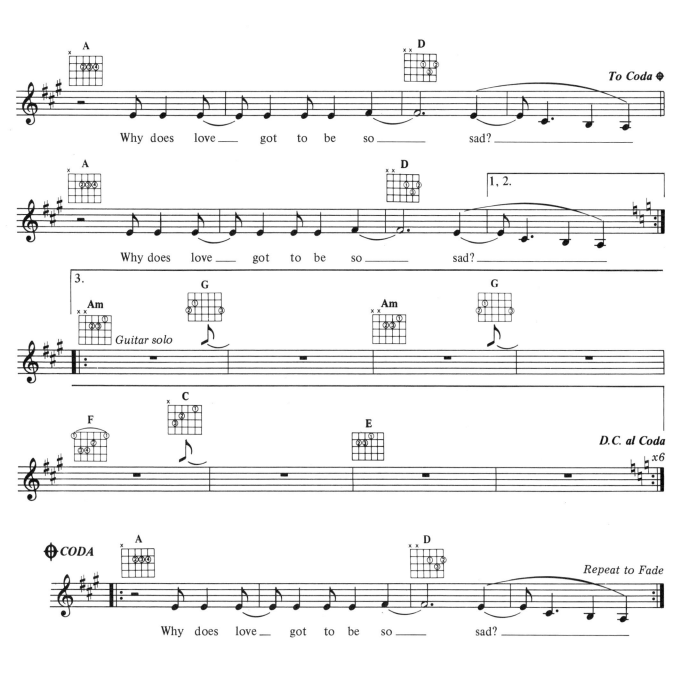

Why does love ___ got to be so _____ sad? _____

Verse 2
Like a moth to a flame,
Like a song without a name,
I've never been the same since I met you.
Like a bird on the wing,
I've got a brand new song to sing.
I can't keep from singing about you.

Verse 3
I'm beginning to see,
What a fool you've made of me,
I might have to break the bus when I find you.
Stop running away.
I've got a better game to play.
You know I can't go on living without you.

Motherless Children Traditional. Arranged by Eric Clapton & Carl Radle

4/4 Rhythm/Strumming/Swing/Damp down strokes
See Course Book No. 4 Page 11

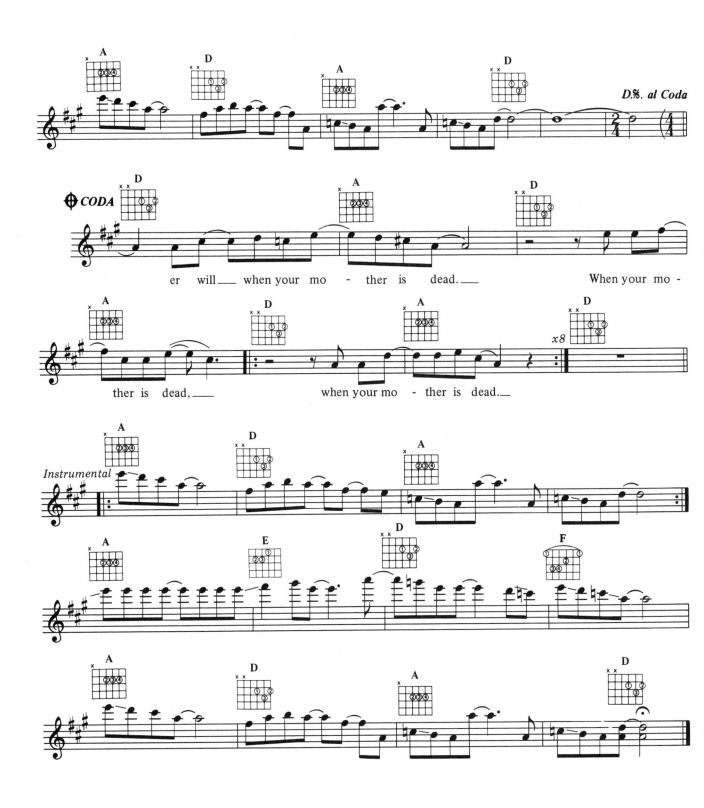

Book 4

Verse 2 on %.
Sister will do the best she can
When your mother is dead Lord
Sister will do the best she can
When your mother is dead Lord.
Sister will do the best she can.
So many things a sister can't understand.
Nobody treats you like a mother will
When your mother is dead Lord.

Sunshine Of Your Love

Words & Music by Jack Bruce, Pete Brown & Eric Clapton

4/4 Rhythm/Damping technique with embelishments
See Course Book No. 4 Pages 11 and 16-22

ing so— long   to — be where— I'm go - ing   in — the sun-

shine of   your   love. _____   I'm

Guitar Solo over continued phrase

D.%. al Coda

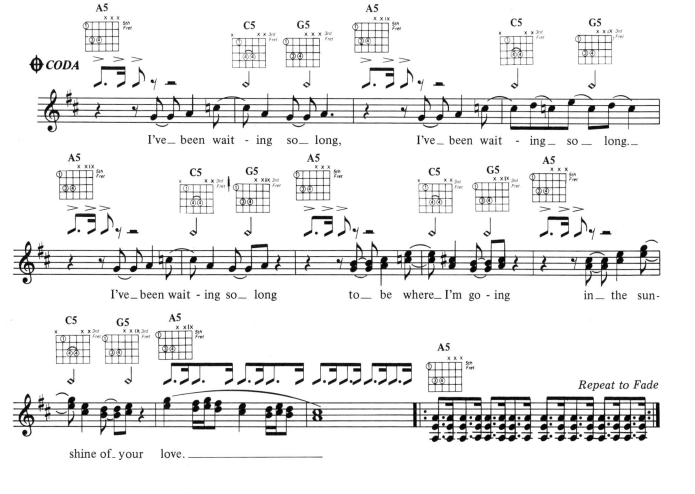

I've_ been wait - ing so_ long, I've_ been wait - ing_ so_ long.

I've_ been wait - ing so_ long to_ be where_ I'm go - ing in_ the sun-

shine of_ your love. _____

Repeat to Fade

Verse 2
I'm with you, my love,
The light shining through on you
Yes, I'm with you my love.
It's the morning and just we two.
I'll stay with you darling, now
I'll stay with you 'till my seeds are dried up.

Verse 3 on %. — as Verse 2

Miss You

Words & Music by Eric Clapton, Greg Phillinganes & Bobby Columby

4/4 Rhythm/Damping/Accented off beats
See Course Book No. 4 Page 11

Moderate rock

Don't change your mind;_ I ain't got the time_ to sit and_ won-der.

I'm do-in' fine;_ you de-cide to leave_ I won't go_ un-der.

You know I've come this far with-out_you. It won't be too hard to be_ a-lone._____

I've got choi-ces all a-round_ me, so I won't be spend-ing too much time_ at home.

CHORUS

_ Still, I'm gon-na miss you._ I'm gon-na miss you, ba-by, yeah._

I can't for-give _ you _ Still, I'm gon-na miss you, ba - by
miss you ba - by.

Verse 2
No, don't say a word
I already heard that you don't love me.
In your state of mind
I don't need to hear your side of the story.

Your friends all said we had a future,
But I don't think I really want to know.
Our friends keep telling me to lose you,
And how glad they'll be when you decide to go.

Layla Words & Music by Eric Clapton & Jim Gordon

4/4 Rhythm/Strumming/Figures and embelishments
See Course Book No. 4 Pages 16-23 and 26

CHORUS *(with guitar figure)*

Repeat for slide 12^{x} guitar solo al fine

Guitar figure as for the Chorus

Verse 2
Tried to give you consolation,
And your old man won't let you down.
Like a fool, I fell in love with you
Turned the whole world upside down.

Verse 3
Let's make the best of the situation
Before I finally go insane
Please don't say we'll never find a way,
And tell me all love's in vain.

Let It Grow Words & Music by Eric Clapton

4/4 Rhythm/Alternative thumb
See Course Book No. 4 Page 14

CHORUS *Rhythm Strum*

Let it grow, let it grow. let it blos-som, let_ it flow.

In the sun,_ the rain,_ the snow, love is love-ly, ___ so let_ it grow.

(let it let_ it grow.

Instrumental

grow)

Instrumental Electric Guitar

CODA

Let it, let it grow, let it grow, let it blos-som, let_ it

flow. In the sun_ the rain,_ the snow, love is love - ly, ___ let_ it

Repeat and Fade

grow.

Verse on 𝄋.
Time is getting shorter,
There's much for you to do;
Only ask and you will get what you are needing,
The rest is up to you;
Plant your love and let it grow.

Peaches And Diesel

Words & Music by Eric Clapton & Albhy Galuten

4/4 Rhythm/Syncopated Arpeggios
and embelishments for 2 Guitars
See Course Book No. 4 Pages 16-23

Roll It Over   Words & Music by Eric Clapton & Bobby Whitlock

4/4 Rhythm/Blues
See Course Book No. 4 Page 8

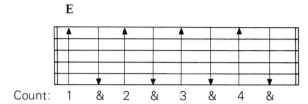

Count: 1   &   2   &   3   &   4   &

Guitar 2 — figure

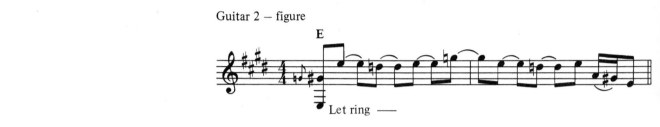

Let ring —

Moderate blues

Go down ea-sy   and let me take my time. ___   Go down ea -

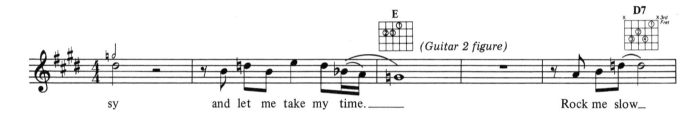

sy   and let me take my time. ___   Rock me slow __

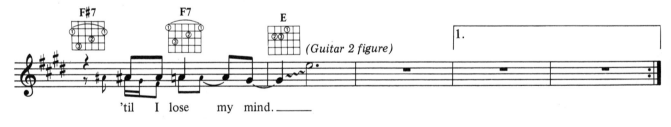

'til I lose   my mind. ___

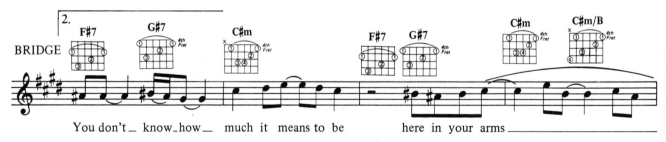

You don't_ know_how_ much it means to be   here in your arms ___

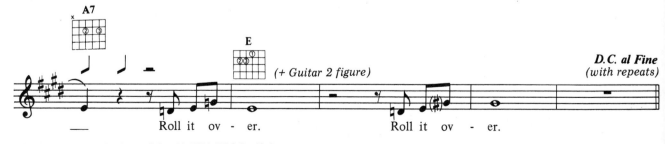

D.C. al Fine
(with repeats)

___ Roll it ov — er.   Roll it ov — er.

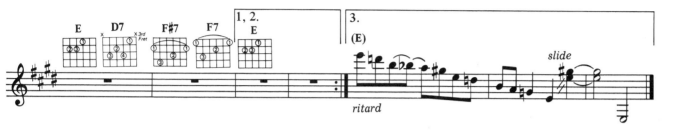

Verse 2
Roll it over,
Let's take it from behind
Roll it over,
Let's take it from behind
S'only love
God knows it ain't the crime.

Verse 3 (D.C.) — as Verse 1
Verse 4 — as Verse 2

Got To Get Better In A Little While

Words & Music by Eric Clapton

4/4 Rhythm/Damping + embelishments
See Course Book No. 4 Pages 11 and 16-22

Verse 2
Revolution all across the land
Just like Sly you've got to take a stand
Please don't hurt anybody, don't knock 'em down
Give 'em a helping hand to get up off the ground.

Verse 3 — Guitar solo

Verse 4 — Guitar solo al CODA

Printed by Printwise (Haverhill) Limited, Suffolk 12/04 (53405)